Across the Curriculum
GEOGRAPHY
for ages 6 – 7

on

wide range of specially devised
geography units, that can be used
ng geography. Alternatively, you
ng other subjects, in the
e aspects of the geography

and a set of Teacher's Notes.
be made to other subjects, to
ell come up with more ideas and
g. The Teacher's Notes provide
d details of the Numeracy and
each sheet covers. A summary of
age overleaf.

be centred around first hand
and in the local area. Some of the
fically for these activities. Some
worksheets, which do not have a specific geographical content, are included
because the geography topic being covered provides obvious and important
links to aspects of other subjects.

Another fundamental aspect of learning at KS1 is the use of discussion to
facilitate learning. Many of the worksheets will be invaluable for speaking and
listening – an important aspect of English in the National Curriculum that is
not always addressed through the Literacy Strategy. Most of the worksheets
can be used as a focus for small group activities and are ideal for children
working with teaching assistants.

Contents and Curriculum Links

WORKSHEET	GEOGRAPHY	OTHER CURRICULUM OBJECTIVES
Living on an island 1	2d, 3d	Literacy: Term 1 Text 1, 5
Living on an island 2	2d, 3d	Literacy: Term 1 Text 1, 5
Living on an island 3	2d, 3d	Literacy: Term 1 Text 1, 5
Living on an island 4	2d, 3d	Literacy: Term 1 Text 1, 5
Living on an island 5	2e	Literacy: Term 1 Text 13
Where's that bear? 1	1a, 1c	Literacy: Term 1 Word 10, Term 2 Word 10, Term 3 Word 9
Where's that bear? 2	1c	Literacy: Term 2 Word 4
Where's that bear? 3		Numeracy: Shape and Space Symmetry
Where's that bear? 4		DT 2b, 2c, 2d, 5b
The Seaside 1	1c, 3a	Literacy: Term 3 Text 13
The Seaside 2	1c	History 2a, 2b, 4a, 4b
The Seaside 3	1c, 3a	Art 1, 2b
The Seaside 4		Music 1a, 4a, 4b, 5a
Global eye 1	1c	Literacy: Term 1 Word 10, Term 2 Word 10, Term 3 Word 9
Global eye 2	1c	Numeracy: Calculations 'Tables' facts
Global eye 3		DT 1a, 2a, 3a, 4a, 5b
A contrasting locality overseas 1	2a	Literacy: Term 1 Word 10, Term 2 Word 10, Term 3 Word 9
A contrasting locality overseas 2	2a, 2c	Literacy: Term 1 Word 10, Term 2 Word 10, Term 3 Word 9
A contrasting locality overseas 3	2c	Numeracy: Measures
A contrasting locality overseas 4	2c	Numeracy: Measures
Our whole world 1	2a, 2c, 3b	Literacy: Term 1 Word 10, Term 2 Word 10, Term 3 Word 9
Our whole world 2	2a, 2c, 3b	Literacy: Term 1 Word 10, Term 2 Word 10, Term 3 Word 9
Our whole world 3	2c, 3b	You will establish your own connections
Our whole world 4	2c, 3b	You will establish your own connections
Our whole world 5	2d, 3e	Literacy: Term 1 Word 10, Term 2 Word 10, Term 3 Word 9
Our whole world 6	2d, 3e	Literacy: Term 1 Word 10, Term 2 Word 10, Term 3 Word 9
Our whole world 7	1a, 2c, 3b, 3d, 4a	Literacy: Term 1 Text 5, Term 2 Text 5
Our whole world 8	1a, 2c, 3b, 3d, 4a	Literacy: Term 1 Text 5, Term 2 Text 5
Geography and numbers 1	2a, 2d	Numeracy: Organising and using data
Geography and numbers 2	1b, 2a	Numeracy: Numbers and the number system
Geography and numbers 3	1b, 2a	Numeracy: Numbers and the number system; Science Breadth of study 1c, 2a; Literacy: Term 1 Sentence 9, Term 2 Sentence 5
Geography and numbers 4	1a, 1b, 2a, 2b	Numeracy: Organising and using data; Literacy: Term 1 Word 9, Term 2 Word 9, Term 3 Word 8; Science: Scientific enquiry 1

Living on an island

CURRICULUM LINKS

We show possible curriculum links but we will not have thought of everything so you may like to add some of your own.

GEOGRAPHY
- Locate the Caribbean on a world map
- Find the names of West Indian islands
- Find the equator on a map – compare distance to the equator of West Indies/Britain
- Climate of the West Indies
- Ways of travelling to the West Indies

LITERACY
- Comprehension (Worksheet 1, 2, 3, 4, 5)
- Vocabulary connected with islands and tropical climate

SCIENCE
- Link crops of West Indian islands to healthy eating

MUSIC
- Opportunities to listen to steel band music
- Pupils can improvise their own band using class percussion
- Investigate Caribbean songs and rhymes (see *Mango Spice* songbook*)

NUMERACY
- Mathematical language of direction

PE
- Dance activities based on 'Jimmy's island' story and on steel band sounds

Living on an island

DT
- Making a vehicle to carry a banana or other piece of tropical fruit

HISTORY
- Links with 'seaside holidays in the past'

ART
- Looking at the vibrant colours in Caribbean art
- Focus on nature found in Caribbean art
- Sculpture based on pupils' ideas about tropical islands

ICT
- Making 'binary trees' using a selection of tropical fruits

* *Mango Spice: 44 Caribbean Songs* published by A & C Black

Living on an island

(QCA Unit 3: An island home)

This unit provides an introduction to life on a Caribbean island. Pupils may have already completed a more basic introduction in the 'Our whole world' unit of *Across the Curriculum Geography for Ages 5-6.*

The Caribbean was chosen as a topic focus as there is a wealth of information available from books, holiday brochures and the internet. The art and music of the Caribbean are very distinctive, making them ideal for study purposes. This area is also ideal when considering geographical similarities and differences between a locality overseas and the pupils' current environments.

Worksheets 1 and 2 (LITERACY) comprise a story based on a fictitious but typical island in the West Indies.

Worksheet 3 (LITERACY) is a comprehension exercise based on the story from sheets 1 and 2. All the questions involve the pupils in choosing the correct answer from four possibilities.

Worksheet 4 (LITERACY) is a more advanced comprehension requiring pupils to write answers. Some questions require pupils to make inferences from the text.

Worksheet 5 (LITERACY) is an outline of the island. It invites children to choose where to place extra items. This provides much opportunity for discussion. You may wish to investigate a range of Caribbean islands and ask the children to add other things to the map of Jimmy's island.

Living on an island 1

Name: Date:

The Surprise

It was Jimmy's birthday. He opened his cards and presents, then had his very favourite breakfast of pancakes and fruit.

Jimmy's mother asked him to take a letter to deliver to his grandma and grandad. It was a long walk and the first time he had been allowed to go alone. As always it was a warm morning and Jimmy set off down the lane.

He passed through the banana plantation. It made him laugh to see the growing bananas protected by bright blue polythene bags.

Just past the edge of the plantation Jimmy could see the waterfall. He heard the water tumbling into the pool below. Soon it would be full of people swimming in the cool, crystal-clear water.

A little further along he stopped to watch a little lizard basking in the mid-morning sunshine. Jimmy wondered what lizards did on their birthdays.

He carried on down the road and soon he could see the blue of the sea ahead of him. The sun was sparkling on the water and Jimmy knew he would soon be at the end of his journey. His grandparents ran a hotel by the beach and Jimmy loved to go there to see them. Sometimes he was taken out in a canoe or a pedal boat and, if he was very lucky, his Grandad would take him round the bay in a sailing boat.

Living on an island 2

Name: Date:

Jimmy walked out of the hot sunshine into the cool shady reception area and said hello to the staff there. They were all smiling slightly as if they had a secret that he didn't know about. No one said "Happy Birthday!".

Jimmy walked across the hotel gardens and opened the door to the house where his grandparents lived. No one was there but a note was on the kitchen table. Jimmy read it.

Happy Birthday Jimmy. Come and find us at the beach near the swimming pool.

So Jimmy set off, still clutching the letter he had to deliver.

When he reached the beach, he found his grandparents waiting for him and smiling. Grandma hugged him as he handed her the letter.

"Close your eyes and count to twenty, Jimmy," she said.

Jimmy closed his eyes and counted. "One, two, three, four, five, six, seven, eight, nine, ten, eleven, twelve, thirteen, fourteen, fifteen, sixteen, seventeen, eighteen, nineteen, twenty." When he opened his eyes he saw his grandparents, parents, aunts, uncles, cousins and friends! At first he could hardly speak as he was so surprised.

"We thought you would like a surprise party," said Jimmy's mother.

Jimmy didn't just like it … he loved it!

Living on an island 3

Name: Date:

Read the story about Jimmy's island.

Answer the questions about the story.

Ring the correct answers.

Jimmy's favourite breakfast was

fruit and toast   cereal and toast   pancakes and milk   pancakes and fruit

What did Jimmy's mother ask him to deliver?

a letter   a parcel   a card   a present

How did Jimmy travel to his grandparents' home?

by bicycle   by car   by walking   by bus

What did Jimmy see basking in the sunshine?

a snake   a lizard   a bird   a banana

What colour was the sea?

brown   sparkling   blue   grey

What could Jimmy go on if he was very lucky?

a canoe   a sailing boat   a speedboat   a pedal boat

To what number did Jimmy have to count with his eyes closed?

ten   twelve   twenty   thirty

What was Jimmy's surprise?

a hug   a present   a swim   a party

Living on an island 4

Name: Date:

Write the answers
to the questions.

What was Jimmy allowed to do that he had never done before?

_____

_____

Name one thing in the story that tells you it takes place in a hot climate.

_____

Why do you think the hotel staff were 'smiling slightly as if they had a secret'?

_____

_____

When Jimmy read the message from his grandparents how did he know which part of the beach to go to?

_____

_____

Was Jimmy pleased about his surprise party?

_____

Living on an island 5

Name: Date:

✎ Here is a map of the island where Jimmy and his family live.
Colour the roads grey. Colour the sea blue.

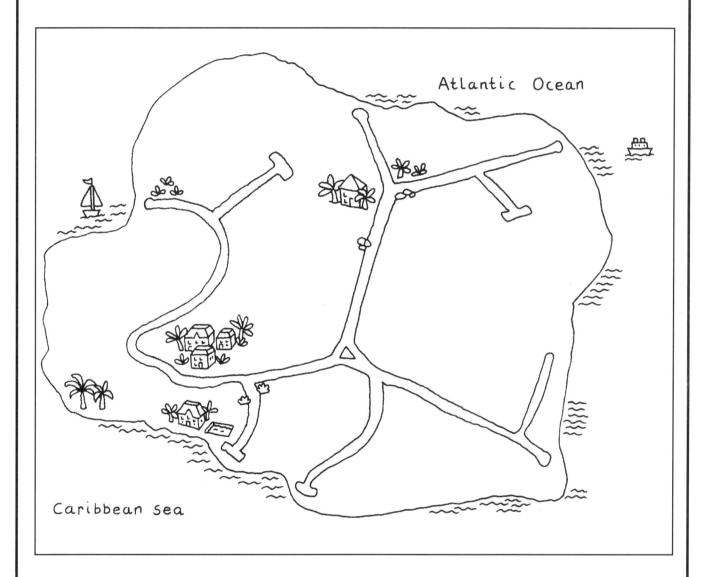

✎ Colour and cut out the items below and stick them onto the map.

Where's that bear?

We show possible curriculum links but we will not have thought of everything so you may like to add some of your own.

LITERACY
- Topic vocabulary (Worksheet 1)
- Compound words (Worksheet 2)

HISTORY
- Link bear's travels to what holidays at the seaside were like in the past

NUMERACY
- Symmetry (Worksheet 3)

MUSIC
- Link instrumental sounds to bear stories and bear puppet show

RE
- Link bear's travels to celebrations

ICT
- Using graphics package to create bear's holiday pictures
- Use of CD ROMS to find information about travel destinations

Where's that bear?

DT
- Puppets – making a hand puppet (Worksheet 4)
- Vehicles – making a vehicle to carry bear

ART
- Bear travel collages with backgrounds based on elements of the natural environment, eg the curved lines found on the surface of stones or shells

SCIENCE
- Link to electricity – making a simple circuit with a bulb to light up bear's home

Where's that bear?

(QCA Unit 5: Where in the world is Barnaby Bear?)

Worksheet 1 (**LITERACY**) encourages children to think about some of the vocabulary used in the topic. This work also provides an introduction to crosswords, including consideration of words going 'across' or 'down' and the importance of knowing how many letters will be found in each answer.

Worksheet 2 (**LITERACY**) deals with the Year 2 requirement for children to understand what compound words are.

Worksheet 3 (**NUMERACY**) provides an opportunity for pupils to gain an awareness of symmetry within the 'Where's that bear?' topic.

Worksheet 4 (**DT**) has some basic instructions and a template for making a bear hand puppet. This work needs to be preceded by practising simple sewing stitches to join two pieces of fabric. The template is symmetrical to make the cutting and matching process easy. The resulting puppet may be given simple holiday clothing, using the templates to cut out and glue on. It is possible to make a 'two-fronted' bear with clothing for the beach on one side and clothing for winter on the other. As extension activities, the children could put on a puppet show or make up a story about their bear.

Where's that bear? 1

LITERACY

Name: Date:

Use the words in the sandcastle. Follow the clues carefully to find out where to write the words.

aeroplane
mountains   beach
travel   suitcase
boat   sandcastles
passport   sun hat
train

Clues across

1 To go on a journey. (6)
2 This transport flies through the air. (9)
4 Pack your clothes in one of these. (8)
5 Very tall hills, sometimes with snow on top. (9)
7 Cross the water in one of these. (4)
8 Build these on the beach. (11)
9 An area of sand by the sea. (5)

Clues down

1 This travels on rails. (5)
3 This little book contains a photograph and information about you. (8)
6 Protect your head from the sun with this. (3,3)

The numbers tell you how many letters are in the words.

   Andrew Brodie: Across the Curriculum Geography 6–7 © A & C Black Publishers Ltd

Where's that bear? 2

Name: Date:

A compound word is made from two shorter words. Teaspoon and football are compound words.

Read the sentences. Underline the compound word in each sentence.

It is important for bear to pack clean clothes in his suitcase.

Bear loves exploring the airport when he travels by plane.

Bear always carries his passport when visiting other countries.

Bear likes to send postcards to his friends at school.

Bear wears his sunglasses on bright sunny days.

He enjoys going for walks in the sunshine.

Bear likes to make footprints in the sand on the beach.

Write the seven words you found in the spaces below.

Where's that bear? 3

Name: Date:

Bear folded things neatly when he packed for his holiday.

Draw what each item looked like when he unpacked it.

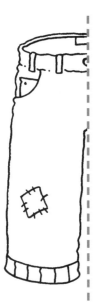

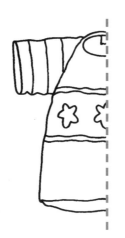

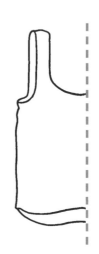

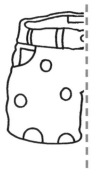

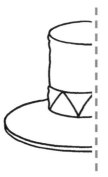

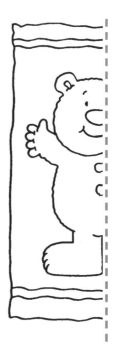

Now colour bear's items.

Where's that bear? 4

Name: Date:

Make a bear hand puppet.

Think about what type and colour of fabric to use.

Sew the back and front of the puppet together.

Add details to make your bear interesting.

The template below will help you.

The seaside

We show possible curriculum links but we will not have thought of everything so you may like to add some of your own.

LITERACY
- Fact/fiction
(Worksheet 1)

MUSIC
- Songs of the sea
(Worksheet 4)

NUMERACY
- Data handling based on places visited by pupils

RE
- Religious festivals and stories with reference to the sea or seaside

ICT
- Writing seaside stories
- Finding information on CD ROM

SCIENCE
- Investigate the way electricity is used at the seaside (to keep ice-cream cold; sea front illuminations; ticket machines, etc)
- Variation – investigating the range of creatures found on the shoreline

The seaside

ART
- Using a viewfinder
(Worksheet 3)

DT
- Puppets – looking at seaside 'Punch and Judy' theatres

PE
- Dance work based on a visit to the seaside

HISTORY
- Seaside holidays 'then and now'
(Worksheet 2)

The seaside

(QCA Unit 4: Going to the seaside)

TEACHER'S NOTES

Worksheet 1 (LITERACY) asks pupils to distinguish between fact and fiction. It also provides a starting point for the topic of 'The Seaside'. The fictional sentences have been designed so that they could all be used in one story if required.

Worksheet 2 (HISTORY) links to the history requirement to learn about seaside holidays in the past. The picture depicts a scene from 1908 and has a number of clear features indicating its age. These include the lack of traffic on the road, the design of the one tram, the ladies with long skirts and the style of the lamppost. Children may also notice the lack of road markings and the lack of modern buildings. The pupils can be asked how many clues they can see that help them to know that the picture is very old. They can also be asked to find Great Yarmouth on a map of Great Britain.

Worksheet 3 (ART) provides an opportunity to consider how 'viewfinder' pieces might look very different from a complete picture. It also encourages pupils to talk about the tropical climate where this picture was taken. (Most pupils will notice the palm trees.) This sheet could lead to children using viewfinders to find unusual frames within pictures taken from holiday brochures.

Worksheet 4 (MUSIC) has a music based theme, although it also has historical links. The original 'Oh I do like to be beside the seaside' was written in 1907 and was often performed in music halls. The chorus of the original song refers to the promenade and to the sound of brass bands that would have been a regular feature of the seaside:

> Oh, I do like to stroll along the prom, prom, prom,
>
> Where the brass bands play, tiddly-om-pom-pom.

The updated words given to the chorus on the worksheet offer opportunities to use instruments to represent the sounds of the sand and the waves. It is a good tune to use to experiment with simple rhythmic accompaniments.

The seaside 1

Name: _____   Date: _____

Look at the eight sentences below. Four of them are facts about the seaside. The other four are sentences taken from a story about the seaside.

✎ Label each sentence with either 'fact' or 'fiction'.

An area of sand where the land meets the sea is called a beach.   ☐

Meg enjoyed making a large sandcastle.   ☐

Paddling in the sea looked like fun; she thought she would try that after lunch.   ☐

Rockpools are sometimes found along the seashore.   ☐

Many people go to the seaside for their holiday.   ☐

The family sat on a large rug to eat their picnic.   ☐

The towns of Minehead, Great Yarmouth, Blackpool and Scarborough are all seaside resorts.   ☐

Meg stood at the water's edge and watched the tiny waves splashing over her feet.   ☐

✎ Find out more facts about the seaside.

The seaside 2

Name: Date:

This picture shows what the seafront at Great Yarmouth was like about one hundred years ago.

Write the correct words on the lines.

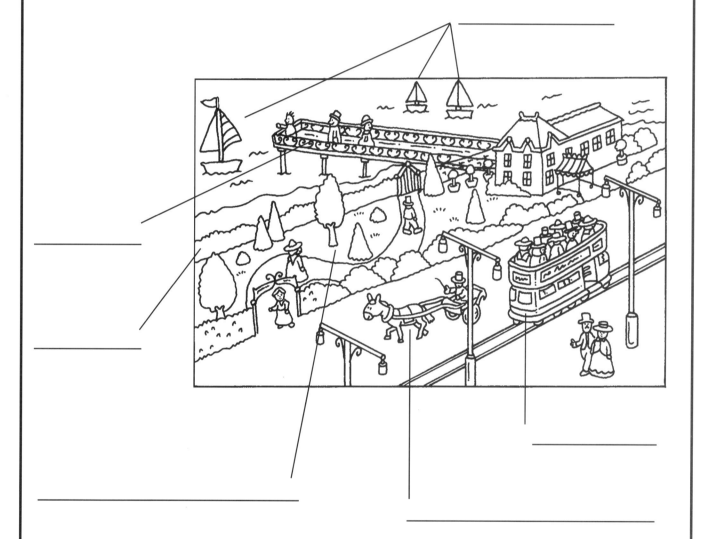

WORD BANK

beach   tram   horse and carriage

pier   formal gardens   yachts

The seaside 3

Name: Date:

✂ Cut out the pieces and arrange them into a complete seaside picture.

Do you think the picture is of Great Britain?

Andrew Brodie: Across the Curriculum Geography 6–7 © A & C Black Publishers Ltd

The seaside 4

Name: Date:

There is a famous old song called 'Oh I do like to be beside the seaside'.

Here are some more modern words that you can sing to the same tune.

Oh I do like to be beside the seaside.

Oh I do like to play upon the sand.

Oh I do like to paddle in the waves as they crash

And jump in the water with a splash, splash, splash.

Oh, just let me lick an ice-cream cornet

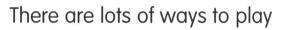

And have the lovely holiday I planned.

There are lots of ways to play

At the seaside every day,

In the waves and

Upon the sand.

Global eye

We show possible curriculum links but we will not have thought of everything so you may like to add some of your own.

LITERACY
- Extending vocabulary
  (Worksheet 1)

NUMERCY
- Data handling – block graphs
- Multiplying twos, fives and tens
  (Worksheet 2)

ICT
- Finding information about: history of spectacles; recycling spectacles; charities that support eye care in developing countries; souvenirs, linking with why Christians give gifts at Christmas

HISTORY
- Looking at pictures and early photographs to trace the history of spectacles

Global eye

DT
- Looking at materials used in spectacles
- Making 'fun specs' (no lenses) to concentrate on ways to join and use hinges
  (Worksheet 3)

SCIENCE
- Link healthy eating to benefits for sight
- Learn that 'eyes can become ill'

Global eye

(QCA Unit 17: Global eye)

In creating the worksheets provided for this unit we have taken two main factors into account:

(i) This unit is intended for higher attaining pupils in Year 2.

(ii) Most of the resources for study may be obtained through appropriate charities, so we have concentrated on curriculum objectives that are unlikely to be covered by other sources.

Worksheet 1 (**LITERACY**) is designed to ensure that pupils have a clear understanding of the vocabulary specific to this topic.

Worksheet 2 (**NUMERACY**) focuses on the objectives to multiply in twos, fives and tens and combines this with a code-breaking element revealing a simple message encouraging the recycling of spectacles.

Worksheet 3 (**DT**) is an instruction sheet asking pupils to design and make spectacle frames. Thin card, that is not too difficult to cut, is ideal for this task. Pupils should be introduced to a variety of ways of joining card to make frames that can fold flat. Discuss measuring the width of faces and lengths from front of frames to ears to ensure a reasonable fit. Encourage the children to decorate the frames – perhaps a theme for this could be introduced.

Global eye 1

Name: Date:

Follow the clues to find the correct answers. The words you will need are in the word bank.

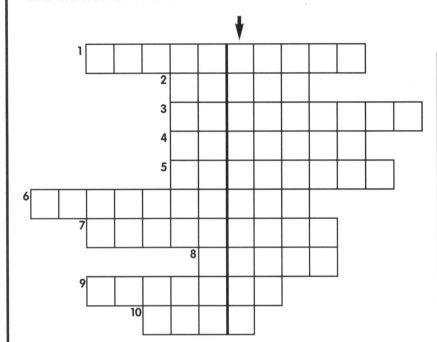

WORD BANK

blind   optician

pupil   microscope

telescope   recycle

iris   glasses

binoculars   eyelashes

1   Use this to see very small things.
2   Light enters the eye through this.
3   Tiny hairs that grow along eyelids.
4   Do this to glass, paper, aluminium, spectacles and other items that you don't need any more.
5   This person will examine eyes.
6   Use these to view distant objects.
7   Look through this long tube to make distant things seem closer.
8   Unable to see.
9   Many people wear these to improve their sight.
10 The coloured part of the eye.

If your answers are correct you should see another word meaning 'glasses' reading down the bold column. Write it below.

— — — — — — — — — —

Global eye 2

Name: Date:

✎ Answer each calculation.

Find the letter in the code that matches each answer.

Use the letters you have found to spell out a message. Write it on the lines below. The puzzle has been started for you.

A	B	C	D	E	F	G	H	I	J	K	L	M
30	2	18	8	20	5	50	12	90	25	45	10	60

N	O	P	Q	R	S	T	U	V	W	X	Y	Z
35	16	4	6	70	15	14	88	80	55	40	100	99

word one

1. $7 \times 10 = 70$ [R]   2. $10 \times 2 = 20$ [E]   3. $9 \times 2 = $ □

4. $10 \times 10 = $ □   5. $9 \times 2 = $ □   6. $5 \times 2 = $ □

7. $2 \times 10 = $ □

word two

1. $3 \times 5 = $ □   2. $2 \times 2 = $ □   3. $4 \times 5 = $ □

4. $9 \times 2 = $ □   5. $7 \times 2 = $ □   6. $3 \times 10 = $ □

7. $2 \times 9 = $ □   8. $2 \times 5 = $ □   9. $2 \times 10 = $ □

10. $3 \times 5 = $ □

word three

1. $7 \times 2 = $ □   2. $8 \times 2 = $ □

word four

1. $6 \times 2 = $ □   2. $10 \times 2 = $ □   3. $5 \times 2 = $ □   4. $2 \times 2 = $ □

word five

1. $8 \times 2 = $ □   2. $7 \times 2 = $ □   3. $6 \times 2 = $ □

4. $2 \times 10 = $ □   5. $7 \times 10 = $ □   6. $3 \times 5 = $ □

_ _ _ _ _ _ _   _ _ _ _ _ _ _ _ _ _   _ _

_ _ _ _   _ _ _ _ _ _ _ .

Global eye 3

Name: Date:

You are going to design and make some spectacle frames.

You have a selection of materials to choose from.

Your spectacle frames should fold flat for storage.

Your spectacle frames should fit your head.

Try to make your spectacle frames look interesting.

My Fun Spectacles

A contrasting locality overseas

CURRICULUM LINKS

We show possible curriculum links but we will not have thought of everything so you may like to add some of your own.

RE
- Considering the beliefs and religions of the chosen locality

LITERACY
- Topic vocabulary
  (Worksheet 1, 2, 3)

PE
- If appropriate, dance and movement from the chosen locality

DT
- Examining the way buildings are constructed in the chosen locality

A contrasting locality overseas

NUMERACY
- Distances on a map – comparing using non-standard measures
  (Worksheet 4)

MUSIC
- Songs from the region

ART
- Examining examples of art from the region of the contrasting locality- creating pictures/ sculptures in a similar style

SCIENCE
- Temperature – observing temperatures in the school grounds to enable pupils to make comparisons to their contrasting locality
- Considering the materials used in the construction of homes and other buildings
- Diet – comparing pupils' diets to diets of children in the chosen locality overseas

A contrasting locality overseas

(QCA Unit 22: A contrasting locality overseas - Tocuaro)

TEACHER'S NOTES

QCA guidance for geography suggests that Year 2 pupils could study the village of Tocuaro in Mexico, the island of St Lucia or a family in Bangladesh. Teachers can, however, base the work on a different area of their own choice. The focus of the work is to improve pupils' understanding of other places through making comparisons with their own area. The QCA unit also suggests that children should be able to locate the chosen location on a map of the world and to identify the main continents and oceans.

Worksheet 1 (LITERACY) contains the vocabulary of the main continents and oceans. The children will benefit from much discussion in which the features that distinguish continents and oceans are made clear and the names of the continents and oceans are mentioned repeatedly. Note that we have used the name 'Australia' as a continent, based on the definition of a continent as a continuous body of land. Some textbooks refer to Australasia or Oceania as titles for this area of the world, containing many islands in the South Pacific. It would be helpful for pupils to complete this sheet following the discussion but before working on worksheet 2.

Worksheet 2 (LITERACY) consists of a map of the world. The children should colour the land green and the sea blue, following the conventions of mapping. The names of the main continents and oceans should be entered in the appropriate places.

Worksheet 3 (NUMERACY) shows a map of the world with certain well-known cities marked on. Please mark on the position and name of your chosen 'contrasting locality overseas', prior to photocopying. You may wish to ask a classroom assistant to work with a small group of children to complete these activities. The children should measure the distances from London to each of the cities using pieces of thread or strips of paper, cutting these to match the distance measured. They will use these threads or strips when working on worksheet 4.

Worksheet 4 (NUMERACY) is used in conjunction with the map on sheet 3. The children will write the name of the appropriate city at the end of each line representing distance from London. They will need to draw a line to show the distance to the chosen contrasting locality. We do not recommend measuring the lines in centimetres as this will cause complicated discussions related to scale. At this stage we are encouraging pupils to make comparisons of distance, observing for example that Paris is closer than New York to London.

A contrasting locality overseas 1

Name: _____ Date: _____

Continents are huge areas of land.

Oceans are huge areas of sea.

Sort the words from the word bank and write the correct word in each column.

WORD BANK

Australia   South America   Pacific   Europe   North America

Atlantic   Asia   Indian   Africa

Continents	Oceans
_____	_____
_____	_____
_____	_____
_____	
_____	

Name: **Date:**

Continents and oceans

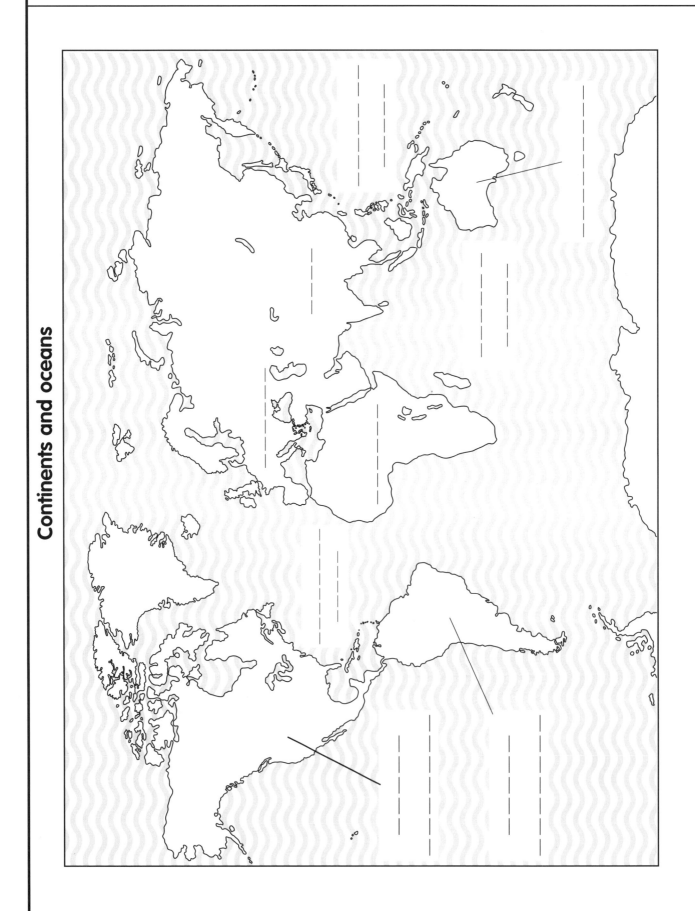

A contrasting locality overseas 3

Name: Date:

World cities

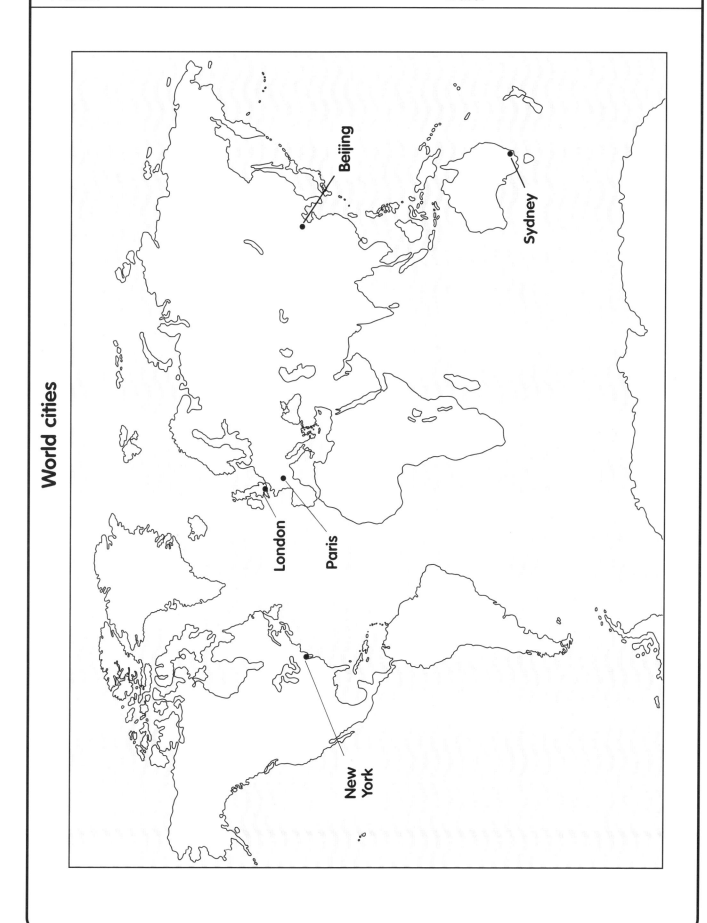

Beijing

Sydney

London

Paris

New York

A contrasting locality overseas 4

Name: Date:

Look at the map on Worksheet 3. Measure the distance on the map from London to:

New York   Sydney   Beijing   Paris

The lines below represent the distances from London to these other cities. Write the names of the cities in the correct places. Draw the missing line – make sure that it is the correct length.

London   London   London   London

Our whole world

CURRICULUM LINKS

We show possible curriculum links but we will not have thought of everything so you may like to add some of your own.

LITERACY
- Vocabulary: names of countries of the British Isles; names of the capital cities (Worksheet 1, 2)
- Reading and comprehension: stories from other countries (Worksheet 6, 7, 8, 9)

ICT
- Writing sentences on the computer
- Finding information from CD ROM

NUMERACY
- Distances on world maps – link back to the 'contrasting locality overseas'
- Distances on maps of the British Isles – eg comparisons of distances to holiday destinations or to homes of relatives

SCIENCE AND DT
- Diet and food from other parts of the world (Worksheet 4, 5)
- Observation of local buildings; what are they made from? Where do these materials come from? (eg wood from countries with lots of forests; slate from Wales, Spain, China or Brazil)

MUSIC
- Songs from other countries, (see *Mango Spice* songbook*)

Our whole world

HISTORY
- Discussing methods of travel, eg how we might travel to the USA or Australia by air – fifty years ago people would travel by ship; how people travel to the seaside – fifty years ago most people would travel by train

PE
- Dance from other countries

ART
- Colouring maps
- Drawing homes, school, shops and other buildings from the local area to create a large wall display map, if this activity has not been completed in Year 1

RE
- Local places of worship

* *Mango Spice: 44 Caribbean Songs* published by A & C Black

Our whole world

(QCA Unit 24: Passport to the world)

Worksheet 1 (LITERACY) consists of an outline map of the British Isles that pupils should colour in the conventional way, i.e. green for land, blue for sea. This is an activity that can be repeated, when relevant to different aspects of geographical work, in order for pupils to become familiar with the shape of the British Isles. It would be helpful to record the weather forecast to remind the pupils of this shape and of the fact that many of them see the shape every day. On this sheet the children are asked to write the names of the countries in the correct places.

Worksheet 2 (LITERACY) is a second copy of the map of the British Isles, this time with the names of countries marked on but with a word bank giving the names of the capitals of each of the five countries. You may wish to add the name of your local town to enable pupils to write it in the appropriate place (a dot on the map will help them with this).

Worksheet 3 provides a copy of a map of the world, with no words marked on, to be used when needed. For example, you may wish to record where foods come from.

Worksheet 4 (LITERACY/SCIENCE) provides a recording sheet to be used on a class visit to a supermarket or greengrocers on which the pupils record where various foods come from. It is essential to make a pre-visit to the shop to ensure that the information is readily available – some shops make the countries of origin very clear.

Worksheet 5 (LITERACY/SCIENCE) is to be used as a follow-up sheet to worksheet 4. As it is to be used in the classroom, there are smaller writing spaces to allow for more detailed information. It would be highly appropriate to use this sheet in conjunction with a world map. Note that some foods may not come from a particular continent as they may come from an island – children could leave the continent column blank for these foods.

Worksheet 6 (LITERACY) provides a reading comprehension passage about a boy living in Kenya. This could be used in a small group reading session in which pupils can be supported in their reading and discussion of the information contained in the passage. They should be encouraged to make comparisons with their own homes and lives.

Worksheet 7 (LITERACY) provides a reading comprehension passage about a girl living in Australia and provides opportunities for discussing the fact that the seasons are at opposite times of the year to ours in the southern hemisphere.

Worksheet 8 (LITERACY) provides a reading comprehension passage about a pair of twins (boy and girl) living in Norway.

Our whole world 1

Name: Date:

✎ Write the names of the countries in the correct places.

| England   Scotland   Wales   Northern Ireland   Republic of Ireland |

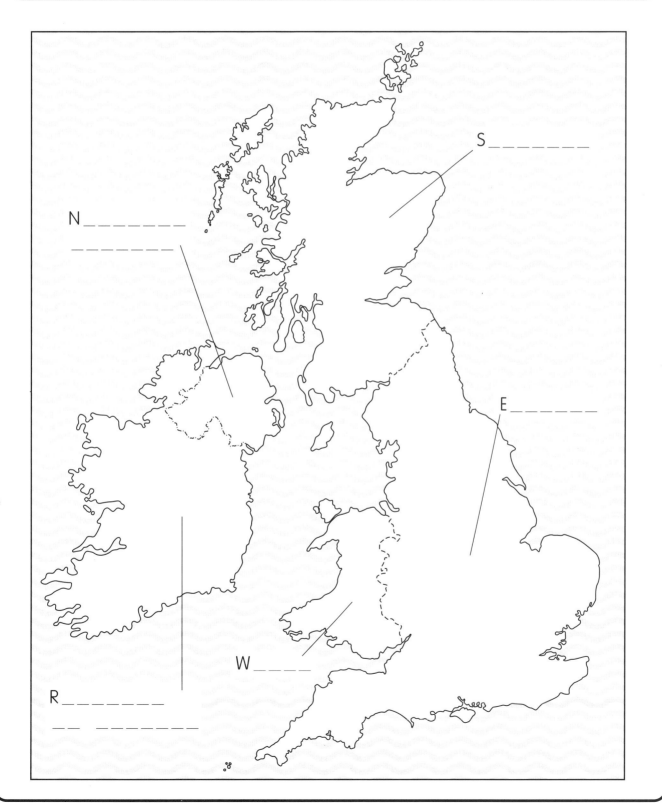

N _ _ _ _ _ _ _ _
_ _ _ _ _ _ _ _

S _ _ _ _ _ _ _ _

E _ _ _ _ _ _ _ _

W _ _ _ _ _

R _ _ _ _ _ _ _ _
_ _ _ _ _ _ _ _

Our whole world 2

Name: _____   Date: _____

✏ Write the names of the cities in the correct places.

> Belfast   Cardiff   Dublin   Edinburgh   London

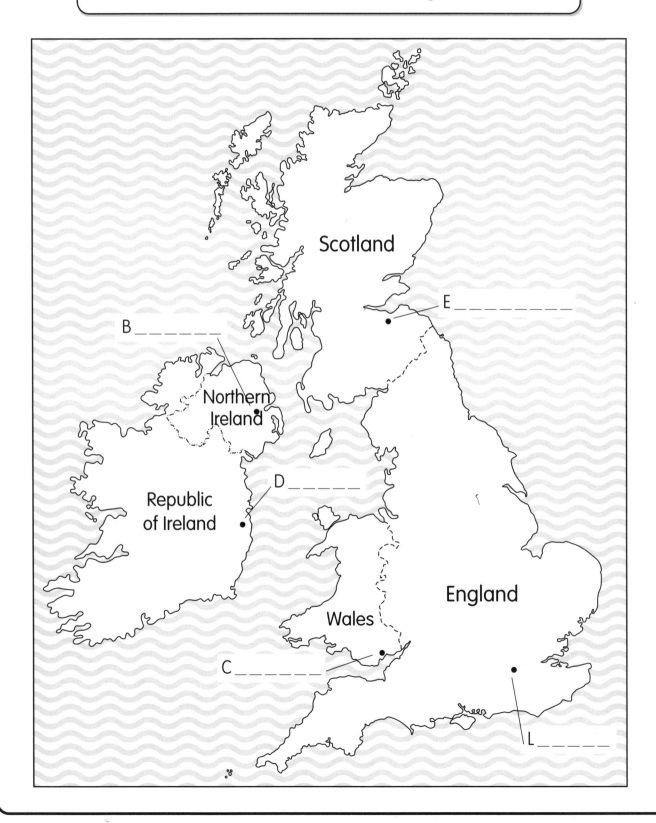

Scotland

E _____

B _____

Northern
Ireland

Republic
of Ireland

D _____

England

Wales

C _____

L _____

Andrew Brodie: Across the Curriculum Geography 6–7 © A & C Black Publishers Ltd

Our whole world 3

Name: Date:

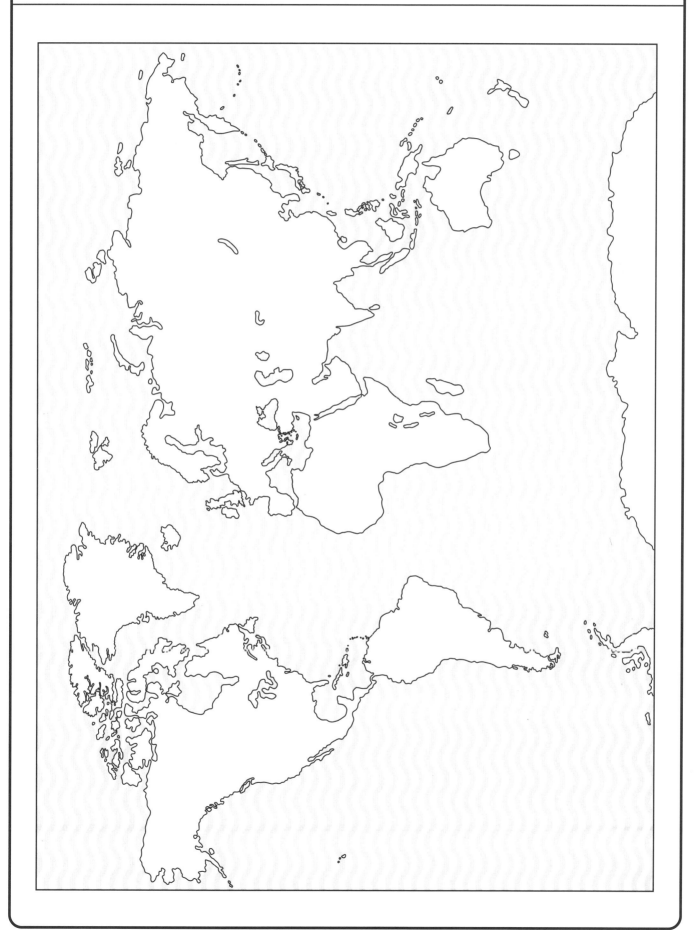

Our whole world 4

Name: Date:

Think about where foods come from. Fill in the table below.

food	country

 Andrew Brodie: Across the Curriculum Geography 6–7 © A & C Black Publishers Ltd

Our whole world 5

Name: Date:

Fill in this table. You can use the words from the word bank to help you.

food	food type	country	continent

WORD BANK

vegetable   fruit   meat   cereal   drink   bread   Australia

Africa   North America   South America   Europe   Asia

Name: Date:

Living in Kenya

Mek lives in Kenya, near the city of Nairobi. He lives in a house that is made of mud that has dried. The roof is made of straw. Mek's house is very comfortable.

The weather is always hot and sunny in Kenya. Mek has his lessons outside, in the shade of a tree.

Mek sees animals near his house. He sometimes sees elephants. He saw a lion once. He is careful by the river because crocodiles live there. Mek is frightened of crocodiles.

Mek loves living in Kenya. He is Kenyan.

Can you find Kenya on a map?

 Kenya is a country. What continent is Kenya in? _____

Name: Date:

Living in Australia

Charlene lives in Australia. She lives in an apartment in Sydney.

Most of the year it is warm and sunny. In the summer the weather is very hot. January and February are the hottest months.

Charlene likes to go to the beach. She swims in the sea but she has to be careful. There are sharks in the sea and there are jellyfish that sting.

Charlene loves living in Australia. She is Australian.

Australia is a country and it is a whole continent.

Can you find Australia on a map?

Name: Date:

Living in Norway

Olaf and Tuva are twins. They live in Norway, in the city of Oslo.

Their house is made of wood. It is very cosy inside because they have a big fire to keep the house warm.

Outside, it is very cold in the winter. There is lots of snow. The days are very short and the nights are very long.

In the summer it is warm. The days are very long and the nights are very short.

Olaf and Tuva love living in Norway. They are Norwegian.

Can you find Norway on a map?

 Norway is a country. What continent is it in? _____

Geography and numbers

We show possible curriculum links but we will not have thought of everything so you may like to add some of your own.

LITERACY
- Topic vocabulary

NUMERACY
- Comparing distances on simple maps, eg world maps, maps of British Isles
- Handling data: continents of origin of certain foods (Worksheet 1)
- Reading a thermometer, seeing it as a number line (Worksheet 2, 3)
- Collecting weather data (Worksheet 4)
- Direction and turning
- Odd and even numbers

ICT
- Use of a floor robot to follow routes
- Discussion using language such as forwards, backwards, turn, half-turn, right, left

Geography and numbers

SCIENCE
- Use of a simple thermometer

Geography and numbers

(QCA Unit 25: Geography and numbers)

TEACHER'S NOTES

Aspects of number have been covered in other topics within this book; for example, measuring and comparing distances on world maps. QCA guidance suggests that pupils should also be encouraged to look for shapes in buildings, to deal with data using tables and block graphs and to read scales on thermometers.

Worksheet 1 (NUMERACY/HANDLING DATA) consists of a block graph with appropriate questions to assist pupils in interpreting the data. The sheet should be used as a focus for discussion in a small group, before pupils answer the questions individually. You may wish to provide a context for the data, using the following:

Tom and Kate went to a supermarket to look at the foods. Their teacher asked the manager if the children could examine the labels and packets. When they got back to school they found out which continents the foods came from. For example, they found that the dates came from Asia, the strawberries came from North America and the grapes came from Europe. They found other foods from these continents and from Africa and Australia. They didn't find any foods from South America. They drew a block graph to show how many foods they had found from each continent.

Worksheet 2 (NUMERACY/SCIENCE) shows a set of thermometers to read. This sheet should be used as a focus for a small group activity under the supervision of a classroom assistant who should discuss the fact that

the thermometer shows temperature. The children will need guidance to understand that the higher the number the warmer the temperature; a warm day in this country might have a temperature of 20° or more while a cold day may have a temperature of 0° or less – facts that are obvious to adults but not to children of Year 2 age. Having completed this sheet, the children can look at a real thermometer, observing the liquid and studying the calibration carefully. The question of negative numbers is extremely challenging for most pupils of this age and we strongly suggest that you use a thermometer similar to the one illustrated, where the negative numbers are arranged downwards – most children will see the logic of temperatures being a certain number of degrees below zero and there will not be a need to refer to 'negative numbers'.

Worksheet 3 (NUMERACY/SCIENCE) shows a set of thermometers to colour to show temperatures. We suggest that this sheet is used on a separate day to worksheet 2 in order to reinforce the concepts. After completing the sheet it would be a good idea if children went outside and observed the temperature on a real thermometer; perhaps they could do this every day for a week, recording what they find on worksheet 4.

Worksheet 4 (NUMERACY/SCIENCE) consists of a recording sheet on which pupils can enter observable data about weather over the course of one school week. It would be interesting for pupils to complete this twice during the school year: once in the winter and once in the summer.

Geography and numbers 1

Name: Date:

Tom and Kate made a block graph of where our foods come from.

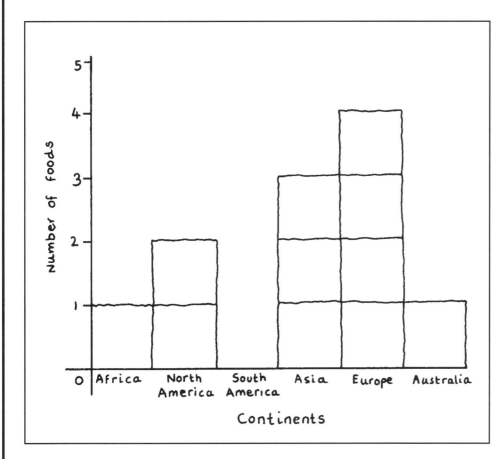

Answer the questions about Tom and Kate's graph.

How many foods did they find from Africa? ☐

How many foods did they find from North America? ☐

How many foods did they find from Asia? ☐

How many foods did they find from Europe? ☐

How many foods did they find from Australia? ☐

From which continent did they find no foods? ☐

Geography and numbers 2

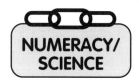

Name: Date:

 Can you read the thermometers? Write the correct temperature under each thermometer.

A
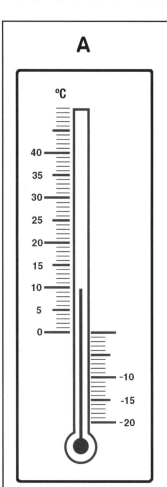

The temperature is

B
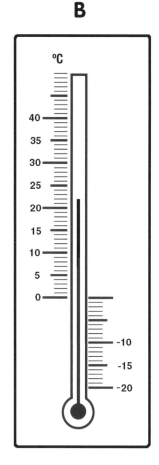

The temperature is

C
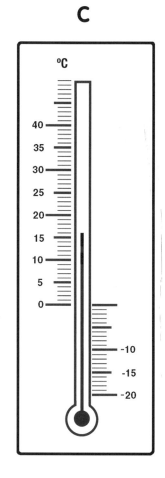

The temperature is

 Which thermometer shows the highest temperature? _____

 In which season would this be? _____

 Which thermometer shows the lowest temperature? _____

 In which season would this be? _____

Geography and numbers 3

Name: Date:

 Show the temperatures on these thermometers.

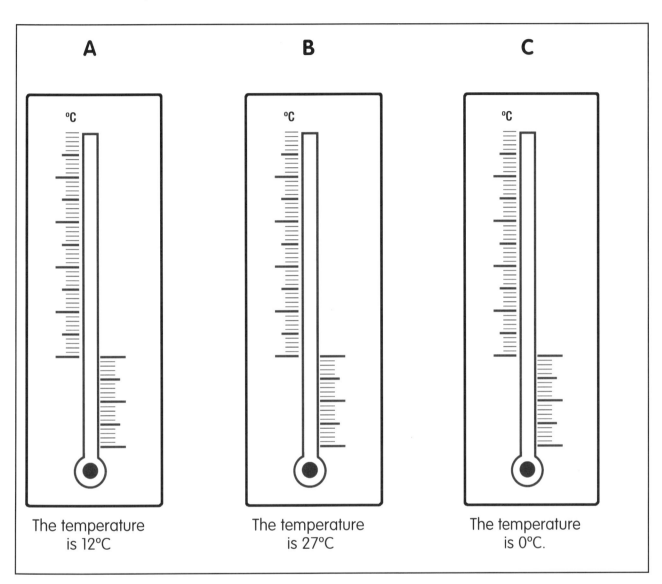

A	B	C
The temperature is 12°C	The temperature is 27°C	The temperature is 0°C.

 Write some sentences about the thermometers. You could say which one shows the highest temperature and which one shows the lowest temperature. You could try to guess the seasons when the temperatures were recorded.

_____

_____

_____

Geography and numbers 4

Name: Date:

The week's weather			
	sunny/cloudy	rainy/dry	temperature
Monday			
Tuesday			
Wednesday			
Thursday			
Friday			